Go, Bee, Go!

JENNIFER B. STITH

See the bee dash.

It has a job.

Go, Bee, go!

The bee can see
so much red!

Bee will lick.

Bee will dip its legs.

See the bee dash back.

Go, Bee, go!

Pack a cell.

Cap it with wax.

Buzz, buzz go
the wings.

Fan the cells.

No, Bee, no!

Not me!

bee	me	see
go	no	so

Decodable Words

back	fan	not
buzz	it(s)	pack
can	job	red
cap	leg(s)	wax
cell(s)	lick	will
dash	much	wing(s)
dip		

High-Frequency Words

a	the
has	with